THE HORRIBLE HEADMONSTER

THE HORRIBLE HEADMONSTER

Poems chosen by Gaby Morgan

Illustrated by Jane Eccles

MACMILLAN CHILDREN'S BOOKS

For Jude – hello sweetheart –
and for Emma Cashmore and Toby Mitchell –
bright stars, thank you.

First published 2001 by Macmillan Children's Books

This edition published 2003 by Macmillan Children's Books
a division of Macmillan Publishers Ltd
20 New Wharf Road, London N1 9RR
Basingstoke and Oxford
www.panmacmillan.com

Associated companies throughout the world

ISBN 0 330 48489 3

3 5 7 9 8 6 4

A CIP catalogue record for this book is available from the British Library.

Typeset by SX Composing DTP, Rayleigh, Essex
Printed by Mackays of Chatham plc, Chatham, Kent.

Contents

First and Foremost

My good points:
I am fresh, novel,
the genuine article.
I am unprecedented.
From the word go
 – a healthy ego;
I'm incomparable,
bold and original.
Never backwards
in coming forwards.
Never put
off to tomorrow
what I can do
today. I rise at dawn
with the cockerel.
I reap the first fruits.
I put my good foot first.
I also first-foot.
I am phenomenal.
First among equals.
I took the first step.
I made the first move.
I always stand up
to be counted.
I don't run away
from the truth.
I get things first
hand; I come straight
to the point.

Hold on, hold on,
I say, *first things first*.
To sum up:
I'm quite exceptional.

My bad points:
I am first
to fly off the handle.
I am selfish, callous,
cruel, ruthless.
I look after number one.
I put myself first.
My friends call me
Numero Uno.

It pains me, but doesn't stop
me pushing
to be first in the queue. *Oh!*
I say snootily,
first come first served.
I don't care for
other numbers.
Useless losers.
I travel first class.
I throw the first stone.
I am tall, lanky,
wear my beret
the French way.
I am Premier.
I am the first in my field.
I show off at first nights.
I believe in yours truly;
the first stroke
is half the battle.
Let's face things
frankly – I am the one
and only.

Jackie Kay

I Would Win the Gold
if These Were Olympic Sports...

Bubble gum blowing
Goggle box watching
Late morning snoring
Homework botching

Quilt ruffling
Little brother teasing
Pizza demolishing
Big toe cheesing

Insult hurling, wobbly throwing
Infinite blue belly button fluff growing

Late night endurance computer screen gazing
Non-attentive open-jawed eyeball glazing

Ultimate volume decibel blaring
Long-distance marathon same sock wearing

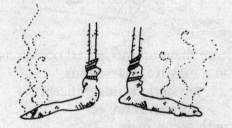

Recognise all these as sports then meet . . .
Me! The Champ Apathetic Athlete!

Paul Cookson

The Collector

Not for me woolly dolls
or football cards
pop star posters
model cars –
No, I'm into collecting adjectives . . .
    Big, fat, juicy, yummy, scrummy,
    rich and famous
    lean and keen
    kind of words.

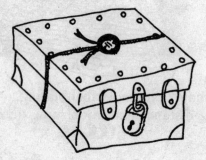

I store them up for special occasions
    in – massive, marvellous,
        mysterious, magnificent
        adjectival boxes
    with secret seals
    and silver keys.

But, at the first stroke of the new millennium
my brother's bedside collection of !!!! marks
exploded with excitement
taking with them
the roof of our house
and
my superb adjective collection.

Request

If you should ever find an adjective
    it is probably mine.
You know the sort of word I mean
    Lonely (cloud)
    misty (lace)
    sprightly (dance)
    pretty (place)
So if you ever see one
I'm sure it will be mine
unless it isn't spelt right
    – or doesn't seem to rhyme.

Peter Dixon

Early Winter Diary Poem
November 18th 1999

Six-thirty;
  winter dawn –

scraping a thin skin
  of frost
from the windscreen –
  numb fingers fumble –
even the spray
  freezes.
The breeze is
  bitter –
It's so cold
  that stones crack –
that wool freezes
  on the sheep's back.

The birds are too still –
  even the sun
turns its back
  on the day;
but lazy wood-smoke
  idles
over Minchin's roof.

Pie Corbett

Limps

Limps lie around
occasionally in pairs
in wait for someone walking
completely unawares

At the sound of a footstep
they prick up their ears
licking their lips
as the victim appears

They whiplash the foot
as it passes by
then sink in their teeth
as you let out a cry

Holding fast to your ankle
they feed off the pain
as you stumble like someone
dragging a chain

And when at last the doctor
says, 'It's only a sprain'
they've scuttled off cackling
to lie in wait again.

Roger McGough

The Horrible Headmonster

A new Headmaster arrives next week
    and rumours about him are rife.
They say he growls like a grizzly bear
    and that he chopped up his wife.

It's said he'll stride and stomp around the school
    like a zombie in the night,
and that his icicle stare can freeze
    hundreds of children with fright.

It's rumoured he wears a skull-shaped ring,
    and a tie with nests of fleas.
When he smiles he shows razor-sharp fangs.
    There are tattoos on his knees.

We've heard that he has a werewolf's howl.
There's a jagged scar on his cheek.
They say that he owns a whippy cane
    and that he'll use it next week.

Already he's called the 'The Headmonster'
    and some have named him 'The Ghoul'.
We'll soon find out if the rumours are true
    when he arrives at our school.

Wes Magee

13

Disguise

Every morning after I shampoo my fur
I climb into my humanskin costume and
Put on my human mask and human clothes.

Then I go out into the human city
And catch a human bus to work.

As I sit at my computer
Summoning up images of the financial world
None of my colleagues know
That inside my human hand gloves
Are the brown and burly
Sharp and curly
Paws of a grizzly bear.

Yes, I am a bear in cunning disguise,
Only passing as human
Trying not to yield to temptation
As I lumber past
The sticky buns in the baker's shop
The honeycombs in the health shop

I am married to a human woman who knows my secret
We have a human daughter
Who is rather furry and has deep golden eyes
And gentle paws
We call her Bruinhilda

I took Bruinhilda to a circus once
But there was a performing bear
Riding a unicycle, juggling with flames
Dancing to an accordion

I sat tight
Though she might have been my mother
I sat tight
While the inside of my human mask
Filled up with the tears of a bear.

Adrian Mitchell

Burying Moses

Moses was very old,
Ninety-eight, my grandpa said,
So we shouldn't cry too much
Now poor old Moses was dead.

Moses used to be black
But he slowly turned grey as a fog,
And snuffled and wheezed and snored.
Moses was our old dog.

Each year that people live
Counts for a dog as seven.
'He was a good old boy,' said Grandpa,
'He's sure to go to heaven.

'But first we must go and bury him
At the back of the garden shed,
So come and give me a hand;
We'll make him a deep warm bed.'

And so we lowered old Moses
Down in the hole Grandpa dug,
And he huddled there in a bundle
Like a dusty old fireside rug.

Then we filled in the hole and patted
The soil down smooth and flat.
'I'll make him a cross,' said Grandpa.
'The least we can do is that.

'He'll be wagging his tail in heaven,
So you mustn't be too upset . . .'
But Grandpa's voice sounded croaky,
And I could see his old cheeks were wet.

Vernon Scannell

Up on the Roof

Up on the roof of a church
was a small, blond boy
and a black and white kitten.

Down below, the priest
was praying aloud,
pleading with God,

asking him to keep
this small boy from falling
down from his church.

He couldn't phone the mother
as he didn't know her,
and cats all looked the same.

When the verger appeared
with a telescopic ladder
the priest closed his eyes

and, gripping his rosary,
he prayed in the dark until
the verger began to climb.

The boy was on his feet now
calling the kitten
who refused to move.

'Sit down,' begged the priest,
in an almost whisper
so as not to alarm the boy

who paid no attention,
walking over the slates
as if on the pavement

or as if he had wings –
with the sun in his hair
he looked like an angel.

When the verger's bald head
rose above the drainpipe
the boy had the kitten

and was walking back,
along the ridge,
with a beatific smile.

Matthew Sweeney

Mammoth Tasks, Or –
Why the Mammoth Became Extinct

Eat grass.
Eat more grass.
Rub tusks on tree trunk.
Eat grass.

Make huge hairy trumpeting noise
With my lovely mammoth trunk –
Attract beautiful lady mammoth
Make mammoth music together,
Make baby mammoths,
So that mammoth kind will never vanish from the earth …
Later.

Right now
Eat grass.

Jan Dean

chomp
munch

Jack in the Sky

Jack popped his head through a door in the sky
Hopped down Memory Street
Raised his hat to the smiling sun
And the friends he chanced to meet.

He danced in the eye of the afternoon
Smiled at all he saw
While the cat on the sun-warmed doorstep purred
And licked her folded paw.

Jane on a swing in the garden green
Her yellow hair flowed free
Smiled at the ghost of brother Jack
That only she could see.

Gareth Owen

For Years I Asked Uncle Harry

For years I asked Uncle Harry
Why he wouldn't, but he'd just say,
'Maybe I will sometime soon,
I'm not in the mood today.'

But I pestered my Uncle Harry
Till eventually he did,
And suddenly there was chaos,
The cat ran away and hid

Inside the Rottweiler's kennel,
The fish all jumped out of the pond,
The parrot in its cage screamed, 'Let me out!'
And the blackbird in the garden went blond.

A squirrel in a tree near the window
Just keeled over and died,
And the doctor's been treating me for shock
Since my Uncle Harry smiled.

Valerie Bloom

Mistress Cooper

A hat-fanatic, a hat-fanatic,
Mistress Cooper is a hat-fanatic,
every hat she sees she has to have it.
Who knows how she got the hat-habit.

High hats, low hats,
fat hats, skinny hats,
springy hats, frilly hats,
cocky hats, floppy hats.
Hats in hat-boxes, hats on hat-racks,
a hundred and twenty-two to be exact.

'How's that for a hat?' she'll say to you,
whenever she wears a hat that is new.
If you value the friendship of Mistress Cooper
simply answer, 'It's super-dooper.'

Grace Nichols

25

Tasting the Sea

Apparently
there were Cornish sea captains
who could tell exactly where they were
when mist and lack of lights conspired
to hide the coast from view.
When a storm had locked them
on a course for rocks,
they could tell which shore
they were heading towards
by tasting the sea.

And these old soaks,
these old sea rovers
would command the first mate
to hang overboard
and scoop up a cup of sea.
Then holding it up to the light
they'd argue over the colour.
They'd sniff, take a sip,
then swirl it about in the mouth
before spitting it out,
till one of their number
with further thought would announce:

Too bitter for Lizard,
too salty for Sennen,
too clean for Pendeen
too clear for Porthmear

It's here we are, he'd say
with certainty, jabbing a finger
down on the chart.
Then heads would nod
and an order be given
to turn the ship for home,
with a ration of rum for everyone
to celebrate
their escape.

Brian Moses

I Heard the Cuckoo

I heard the cuckoo and I saw him fly,
And that is in my town dreams as I lie
Up in a block whose lights reduce the sky;

As when, to some steep lane, shady and long,
Because I have been, once, part of the throng
Come thoughts and faces that I've lived among.

Jenny Joseph

Perishing

It's down to freezing:
Indoors,
the hunting cat is suddenly tame;
Outside,
late cars
start getting their skates on.

It's five below:
Outside,
windows draw patterns
with broken pencils;
Indoors,
the cat beats us
to the warmest places
and warns us with his eye.

It's ten below:
Indoors,
the cat thrums,
soft
as an oiled engine;
Outside,
puddles
are hardening
their hearts.

David Orme

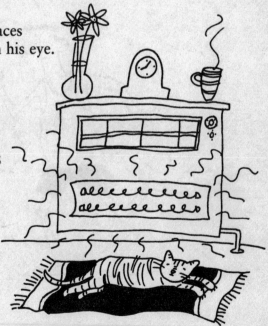

The Prime Minister Is Ten Today

This morning I abolished
homework, detention and dinner ladies.
I outlawed lumpy custard, school mashed spuds
and handwriting lessons.
From now on play-times must last two hours
unless it rains, in which case we all go home
except the teachers who must do extra PE
outside in the downpour.

Whispering behind your hand in class
must happen each morning between ten and twelve,
and each child needs only do
ten minutes' work in one school hour.

I've passed a No Grumpy Teacher law
so one bad word or dismal frown
from Mr Spite or Miss Hatchetface
will get them each a month's stretch
sharpening pencils and marking books
inside the gaol of their choice.

All headteachers are forbidden
from wearing soft soled shoes
instead they must wear wooden clogs
so you can hear them coming.
They are also banned from shouting
or spoiling our assembly by pointing
at the ones who never listen.

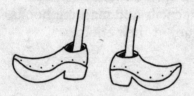

Finally the schools must shut
for at least half the year
and if the weather's really sunny
the teachers have to take us all
to the seaside for the day.

If you've got some good ideas
for other laws about the grown-ups
drop me a line in Downing Street
I'll always be glad to listen
come on, help me change a thing or two
before we all grow up
and get boring.

David Harmer

Fire at Night

It's ready steady sticks for fiery fun,
The strike of the match is the starter's gun.

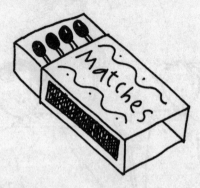

Up go the flames, long-jumping sky,
The smoke catches up, hurdling high.
The crowd stamp their frozen feet
Clap their hands for the winning heat.
Guy Fawkes sits on top of the pyre,
Easily beaten, eaten by fire.
Who is the quickest in the scorching race?
Flames of gold grab first place.
Who beat the day? The crowd then roars
The moon made silver to the stars' applause.
Who has come third? No one remembers,
As they all sprint home, leaving only bronze embers.
As clouds shuffle by with a marathon creep,
Children in bed clutch the prize of sleep.

Andrew Fusek Peters

Penny Piece

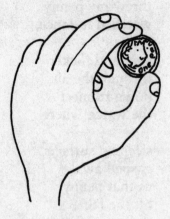

Sun up high,
sky so blue,
went for a walk,
nothing to do.

Branches sighing,
birds a-twitter,
down in the grass
saw something glitter.

Picked it up:
a simple penny,
nothing special,
one of many.

Kept it with me
all the same,
went on careless
till I came

upon a lake
that lay in trance,
threw my penny,
watched it dance,

spin and flicker
through the air,
down to meet
the water, where

sleeping surface
gasped awake
as that penny
hit the lake,

sending out
a circling shiver,
ripples racing,
liquid quiver,

till at last
the glassy pane
slept in silence
once again.

Lake asleep
and penny gone,
made a wish
and then walked on.

Tony Mitton

Mood Manager

Come on LAZY MOOD
let me stay in bed
all day, reading and eating.

Come on SCARY MOOD
see a monster make me scream
something truly awful.

Come on BIG BOLD MOOD
make me beat up
a pensioner's burglar.

Come on SAD MOOD
stop saying remember:
Grandma is dead for ever.

Come on WILLING MOOD:
have me pushing home
a weary wheelchair person.

Come on MEAN MISERY MOOD
make me manage without
touching my pocket money.

Come on GUESSING MOOD
make me guess my wished-for
birthday gift, there parcelled up.

Come on TICKLED MOOD
keep me feeling trumps
answering that quiz correctly.

Come on LUCKY MOOD
make it a lottery win
houseful of money today.

Come on NOISY MOOD
make me holler, shouting:
I passed the test!

James Berry

The Interesting Table

There's a table which stands at the end of the class
With interesting things galore
If it's weird or curious
That's where it goes
It's what 'Interesting Tables' are for.

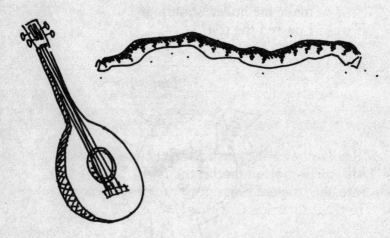

There's an adder's skin, mandolin, thingummyjig
From whatshisname's big sister's house;
A ball signed by Wigan Athletic
And a nit comb with one half-squashed louse.

When we bring something in we discuss it
Then write a poem or two
Miss Bell says it helps to imagine
What interesting objects might feel, say or do.

One day Justin Smethwick turned up with a bag
And a mischievous smile on his face
Then up to the table he boldly went
Put his interesting thing pride of place.

It was . . .

A TOMATO

'Really interesting, Justin!' the class all jeered
Miss Bell's bottom lip hit the floor
And she ushered him out of the classroom
To the interesting corridor.

Lindsay MacRae

Ghost in the School

Winter dark comes early
And the wind attacks the school building
With a vengeance
Hurling sticks and debris at the walls
Invisible fingers try to widen cracks
To find ways in

In the black windows
I see blazing neon reflections
My pale face
And nothing beyond

I hear the howling wind
I hear the creepy cackle of radiators
And was that the tap of a heel?
The snap of a metre stick?
The click of a latch?
The creak of an opening door?
The snicker-snack of brittle bones?

Quickly now.
I hurry to the main door
Am I all alone
In the building?
Alone with the school ghost?

Why are there no teachers working late tonight?
No stragglers from soccer practice?
Where is the caretaker?
Where are the cleaners?
What was that?
I spin round . . .

Roger Stevens

They're Out There

The ghosts of old dragons
Drift over this town,
Their wings grown as thin
As a princess's gown,
Their scaly skin leaf-like
And wintery brown.

The ghosts of old dragons
Are flitting round town.
Their names are lost treasure,
Each glittering noun
Thrown deep in time's ocean
Where memories drown.

The ghosts of old dragons
Keep haunting this town,
Though long-gone like gas-lamp,
Top-hat and half-crown;
Their presence as false
As the face of a clown.

The ghosts of old dragons
Go growling through town,
As upright as tombstones
Engraved with a frown;
With gravel-path voices
Which wind travels down.

Nick Toczek

The Picnic

They biked to the end of the world one day
where the sea tumbled over the brink
and they took out a flask and a couple of cups
and poured themselves something to drink.
They gazed at the waters cascading
in a foaming and terrible wall
and murmured (while spreading a cloth out)
that the world must be flat after all.
They brought out some ketchup and marmite
as a phoenix erupted in flames
and they ate a cheese sandwich with pickle
before they got up for a game.
A unicorn nibbled their cupcakes
as they dribbled a football around
swatting at minuscule dragons
which flew up in swarms from the ground.
As the sun set in fiery glory
and the sea put it out with a hiss,
they cleared up their rubbish and yawning,
tossed it into the abyss.
The night sky was blazing with starlight
as the pair of them cycled away.
They arrived home at three in the morning
and were late in for work the next day.

Marian Swinger

Reading Round the Class

On Friday we have reading round the class.
Kimberley Bloomer is the best.
She sails slowly along the page like a great galleon
And everyone looks up and listens.
'Beautiful reading, Kimberley, dear,' sighs Mrs Scott,
'And with such fluency, such feeling.
It's a delight to hear.'

On Friday we have reading round the class.
I'm the worst.
I stumble and mumble along slowly like a broken-down
   train
And everyone looks up and listens.
Then they smile and snigger and whisper behind their
   hands.
'Dear me,' sighs Mrs Scott, 'rather rusty, Simon.
Quite a bit of practise needed, don't you think?
Too much television and football, that's your trouble,
And not enough reading.'

And she wonders why I don't like books.

Gervase Phinn

The Cruise of the *Bumblebee*

'Twas a wild and windy blustery night
When we shipped on the *Bumblebee*,
Me and Paddy and mad Mick McPhew
All bound for Timbuckthree.

The captain was a scurvy knave
With a black patch on his nose,
He had a hook eye and a wooden-legged parrot
And rings on all of his toes.

The first mate was an ugly swab
His nose was lumpy and fat,
He was four foot four from his bald head to the floor
With a beard like an old doormat.

4 ft 4

The old canal was wild that night
The waves they rocked the boat.
'Switch off the engine!' the Captain cried,
So Paddy untied the goat.

The wind it tore off the Captain's vest
And filled the toilet paper sails,
And Mad Mick sat in the old Crow's nest
A chewin' of his nails.

The Crow didn't like it so she gave him a shove
And tumbled off heading for the deck,
And if the Captain hadn't broken his fall
Poor Mick would have broken his neck.

We did four knots by the old gas works,
We sailed past the coal man's yard,
Then we ran ashore on a rusty old pram
That wasn't marked on the chart.

'All feet on deck!' the captain cried.
'Sorry I mean all hands!
We're sinking quick – a band on ship!'
But we couldn't see any band!

'Every man for himself!' the captain cried
The first mate his prayers did roar.
But me and the lads got some bars of soap
And washed ourselves ashore.

So that was the end of the Captain Bold
And the end of the *Bumblebee*,
And we waited at the old bus stop
For the half-past four bus to Timbuckthree.

Mike Harding

Midnight Meeting

On soft, silent, padded paws,
all cats are grey in the night;
this is their time.

A shadow walking in shadows,
Prometheus is on the prowl.
Other toms keep their distance,
and a fox crosses the road
to avoid him;
but the mouse saw nothing,
heard nothing,
knew nothing.

On wings without a whisper,
old Tawny perches
on the chimney pot,
in time to see the cat
snatch his prey.
Their eyes meet,
the owl and the pussycat,
the staring match of all time.

Prometheus looks away first.
After all,
he has the mouse.

Mike Jubb

Home

East Anglia. Wind whipping in from the sea.
This is the place that is home to me.

    Dunes. Grass so coarse it hurts. Larks
hammering tall spring air over crumbling coastlines.
Views across fenland and heathland: cathedrals like liners
    where smiling angels hover

and other views across broadland in summer to barges
     sewing sky/land seams; and
     towns smelling of malt and hop.
Estuaries glinting like cheap jewellery.

No downs swinging deep into valleys and up to hilltops.
     No steep paths dropping to tiny harbours.

East Anglia. Wind whipping in from the sea.
This is the place that is home to me.

Fred Sedgwick

The Rainmaker Danced

The rainmaker danced
the rainmaker danced
the rainmaker danced.

Down came
the rains
in a flash
and that was the end
of cricket match.

The rainmaker danced
the rainmaker danced
the rainmaker danced

Sky changed
from blue
to grey
and barbecue
was washed away

'What rotten luck!'
cried everyone, faces grim.
But what can you expect
when the rainmaker
was a magical duck
and dying for a swim.

John Agard

Stirring Times

Families weren't small.
Isabella Beeton
could rustle up a meal
just starting with

the head of a hog

a pint of cream

two dozen eggs . . .

and still know
that nothing would be left
uneaten.

Judith Nicholls